TEST 1

A1 How many degrees in a right angle?

2 3 x 1000 =

3 4 – 5 =

4 What is one-third of £24.00?

5 How many lines of symmetry does this shape have?

B1 Multiply £3.75 by 2.

2 16 x 1000 =

3 Is a kilometre longer or shorter than a mile?

4 Divide 5 km by 1000.

5 £1.30 + £1.40 + £1.50 =

C1 If 3 apples cost 36p, how much will 4 apples cost?

2 Divide 3600 by 1000.

3 How many hours in 5 days?

4 A running track of 100m is divided into 8 equal sections. How long is each section?

5 What is the order of rotation of the letter H ?

TEST 2

A1 Put the
the sma

2 6·0 – 1·

3 What is 25% of £100?

4 3·4 + 2·5 =

5 7 x 1000 =

B1 Divide 3 litres by 1000.

2 4·30 – 1·60 =

3 Divide £7.50 by 2.

4 24 x 1000 =

5 Multiply 28 by 3.

C1 A container holds 2·56 litres of salt. How much will 2 containers hold?

2 How many degrees in a triangle?

3 How many lines of symmetry does a regular hexagon have?

4 5 shuttlecocks cost £1.20, how much will 2 cost?

5 Divide 5100 by 1000.

A1 2 x 1000 =

2 4·3 − 2·1 =

3 3·8m + 0·7m =

4 Put these numbers in order, starting with the smallest: −3, −6, −4.

5 How much is $\frac{1}{5}$ of 40cm?

B1 Is an acute angle bigger or smaller than an obtuse angle?

2 14 x 1000 =

3 Multiply £1.25 by 4.

4 Add £0.60, £0.80 and £1.00.

5 Divide 3·8 km by 1000.

C1 Two angles of a triangle are 30° and 40°, what is the size of the third angle?

2 Multiply £3.60 by 100.

3 Divide 7300 by 1000.

4 8 doughnuts cost £2.48, how much will 1 cost?

5 How much is £7.50 divided by 6?

A1 What is 20% of £200?

2 Is this angle acute or obtuse?

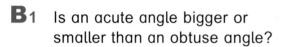

3 7·4 + 1·7 =

4 8 x 1000 =

5 How many lines of symmetry does this shape have?

B1 Divide 10 litres by 1000.

2 Which is longer a metre or a yard?

3 21 x 1000 =

4 −5 − 32 =

5 Divide £5.00 by 4.

C1 Three pairs of identical shoes cost £37.50. How much does each pair cost?

2 What is the total of £2.18 and £1.63?

3 Two angles in a triangle add up to 100°, what is the size of the third angle?

4 Divide 2060 by 1000.

5 How many lines of symmetry does a regular octagon have?

TEST 5

A
1. 5·2 + 3·6 =
2. 1 x 1000 =
3. What is $\frac{1}{10}$ of £30.00?
4. How many degrees in half a right angle?
5. Put these numbers in order starting with the smallest: 3, −2, 1.

B
1. What is the order of rotation of this shape?

2. 36 x 1000 =
3. Add £3.20, £2.40 and £1.70
4. Multiply £1.60 by 3.
5. How many hours in 4 days?

C
1. If a piano has 40 keys and $\frac{1}{5}$ are never used, how many are used?
2. Divide 7·4km by 1000.
3. Total 3·72km and 1·68km.
4. A cup holds 0·62 litres of water. How much would 8 cups hold?
5. What is the total of 62 and 12?

TEST 6

A
1. How much is 25% of £40.00?
2. 8·0 − 2·7 =
3. −6 + 6 =
4. Add £2.60 and £3.30.
5. 9 x 1000 =

B
1. Divide £5.70 by 3.
2. Subtract £1.35 from £5.00.
3. What size is angle x?

4. 50 x 1000 =
5. 37 x 2 =

C
1. A child's building brick weighs 0·8g. How much will 20 weigh?
2. What is 80% of £200?
3. What is the order of rotation of a square?
4. What do the angles in a quadrilateral add up to?
5. Divide 8·5 litres by 1000.

A1 How many lines of symmetry does a capital letter A have?

2 Add £4.20 and £1.70.

3 5 x 1000 =

4 What is $\frac{1}{3}$ of 60?

5 Subtract £3.20 from £5.00.

B1 Divide 9 by 6.

2 62 x 1000 =

3 Put these temperatures in order starting with the coldest: 5°, 3°, −6°, −8°.

4 What is the total of 0·71m, 1·30m and 1·62m?

5 How many millilitres in 12·6 litres?

C1 How much is 40% of £300?

2 Divide 15·6 km by 1000.

3 Divide £1,000,000 by 10.

4 A piece of string 6·3 m long is cut into 7 equal pieces. How long is each piece?

5 What is the total of £4.60, £3.20 and £1.60?

A1 £6.00 − £1.25 =

2 What is 50% of 1?

3 How many degrees are equal to two right angles?

4 What is the total of 0·6, 1·4 and 2·0?

5 7 x 1000 =

B1 Add £4.20 and £12.80

2 74 x 1000 =

3 Does the letter S have a line of symmetry?

4 Multiply £1.40 by 4.

5 What are the total number of days in April, May and June?

C1 What is the size of each angle of an equilateral triangle?

2 Divide 31 litres by 1000.

3 A temperature of −4°C goes down by 3°, what is the temperature now?

4 Reduce 3,000,000 by 600,000.

5 What size is angle x?

A1   2·65cm + 1·30cm =

   2   £3 x 1000 =

   3   Is this angle acute or obtuse?

   4   8)$\overline{64}$

   5   What is one-fifth ($\frac{1}{5}$) of £25.00?

B1   Total 3·62, 1·04 and 1·60.

   2   42km x 1000 =

   3   Divide £9.60 by 3.

   4   How many lines of symmetry does the number 8 have?

   5   Reduce £6.30 by £1.75.

C1   Divide 6·3km by 1000.

   2   Which capital letter of the alphabet has an infinite number of lines of symmetry?

   3   The temperature is 4° but goes down 5°, what is the temperature now?

   4   £12 is shared between 5 boys, how much do they each get?

   5   Does the capital letter Z have any lines of symmetry?

A1   24 x 2 =

   2   What is 75% of £8.00?

   3   Subtract 1·6m from 5m.

   4   £6 x 1000 =

   5   3·8cm + 2·6cm =

B1   Divide £12.80 by 4.

   2   36 litres x 1000 =

   3   Multiply £2.30 by 5.

   4   Put these temperatures in order starting with the coldest: −4°, −8°, −10°, 3°.

   5   How many degrees in 4 right angles?

C1   A child saves up £3.50 for 6 weeks, how much does she have altogether?

   2   How much is 30% of £500?

   3   What size is angle x?

            25°   120°

   4   Divide £3260 by 1000.

   5   Is it possible to have a triangle with two right angles?

When we multiply by 10, 100 or 1000 we can easily see that the numbers have become larger because of the position of the decimal point.

Look at these examples:

3·61 x 10 = 36·1
3·61 x 100 = 361·0
3·61 x 1000 = 3610·0

Notice that when we multiply by 10, the decimal point moves one place to the right from 3·61.

When we multiply by 100, the decimal point moves two places to the right from 3·61 to 361·0.

When we multiply by 1000, the decimal point moves three places to the right from 3·61 to 3610·0.

The decimal point moves the same number of places as there are zeros in the number we multiply by.

Look at these examples
14·29 x 10 = 142·9
because 10 has a single zero the point moves only one place to the right.

14·29 x 100 = 1429·0
because 100 has two zeros, the point moves two places to the right.

14·29 x 1000 = 14290·0
because 1000 has three zeros, the point moves three places to the right.

A 1 3·5 x 10 =

2 4·9 x 10 =

3 6·35 x 100 =

4 6·81 x 100 =

5 4·260 x 1000 =

B 1 3·05 x 10 =

2 4·3 x 100 =

3 7·280 x 1000 =

4 1·27 x 100 =

5 12·30 x 100 =

C 1 0·67 x 100 =

2 3·070 x 1000 =

3 120·70 x 100 =

4 30·800 x 1000 =

5 42·004 x 1000 =

TEST 12

A1 $30 \div 10 =$

2 $3 \cdot 4 \times 10 =$

3 How many degrees in two right angles?

4 $15 \times \frac{1}{3} =$

5 Does 36 plus 36 make 62?

B1 Multiply $3 \cdot 26$ by 100.

2 One-third of a number is 9, what is the number?

3 Divide 700,000 by 100.

4 Two angles of a triangle add up to 106°. What is the third angle?

5 What is the order of rotational symmetry of a rectangle?

C1 What is 30% of £400?

2 Multiply $8 \cdot 070$ by 1000.

3 £1.76 + £0.24 =

4 What is the order of rotation of a regular octagon?

5 One-fifth of a number is 12. What is the number?

TEST 13

A1 Write these fractions in order starting with the smallest: $\frac{1}{2}, \frac{1}{3}, \frac{1}{4}.$

2 $\frac{1}{3}$ of 21 =

3 $7500 \div 100 =$

4 How many 15s in 45?

5 $4 \cdot 8 \times 10 =$

B1 One-fifth of a number is 8, what is the number?

2 Is this angle acute or obtuse?

3 $14 \times 4 =$

4 Multiply $12 \cdot 60$ by 100.

5 Divide £2700 by 100.

C1 One-tenth of a number is 18, what is the number?

2 £3.00 − £1.77 =

3 What is 70% of £200?

4 How many ml in $3 \cdot 25l$?

5 Multiply $10 \cdot 70$ by 100.

A1   5·8 x 10 =

   2   How many 20s in 200?

   3   20 x $\frac{1}{4}$ =

   4   How many ml in 0·6l?

   5   Divide £8.00 by 100.

B1   How many degrees in half a right angle?

   2   131·6 x 10 =

   3   Divide 920,000 by 1000.

   4   One-fifth of a number is 5, what is the number?

   5   26 x 2 =

C1   How much is 15% of £300?

   2   100 x 0·82 =

   3   £3.00 – £1.41 =

   4   One-fifth of a number is 24, what is the number?

   5   Three angles in a quadrilateral add up to 290°. What is the size of the fourth angle?

A1 $\frac{1}{4}$ of 36 =

   2   How many hours from noon on Sunday to midday on Tuesday?

   3   6·3 x 10 =

   4   £6.00 – £2.30 =

   5   7000 ÷ 100 =

B1   Which is larger $\frac{1}{2}$ or $\frac{6}{10}$?

   2   1·46 x 100 =

   3   One-tenth of a number of 6, what is the number?

   4   18 x 3 =

   5   How much is £400 shared by 100?

C1   326·76 x 1000 =

   2   What size is the missing angle?

   3   £2.20 + £3.81 =

   4   What is 18% of £200?

   5   One-tenth of a number is 35, what is the number?

TEST 16

A 1   Divide 1 kilometre by 10.

2   How many cm in 0·3m?

3   9·23 x 100 =

4   3 − 4 =

5   $\frac{1}{5}$ of 40 =

B 1   Divide 820 by 10.

2   76·23 x 100 =

3   One-fifth of a number is 1, what is the number?

4   £2.29 + £1.01 =

5   What size is the missing angle?

C 1   Subtract £1.61 from £10.00.

2   0·404 x 1000 =

3   One-eighth of a number is 9, what is the number?

4   64 x 4 =

5   What is 28% of £200?

TEST 17

A 1   £4.29 + £0.36 =

2   What is one-third of 21?

3   How many 100s in 100,000?

4   5·42 x 10 =

5   How long is 0·9km in metres?

B 1   £1.42 + £1.36 =

2   Share £8400 by 100.

3   391·28 x 100 =

4   One-seventh of a number is 8, what is the number?

5   34 x 3 =

C 1   One-tenth of a number is 23, what is the number?

2   £2.98 + £2.98 =

3   If 8 videos cost £100, how much does each video cost?

4   0·261 x 1000 =

5   15% of an amount is £15, what is the amount?

TEST 18

A 1 $\frac{1}{3}$ of 30 =

2 What size is angle x?

3 How many centimetres are 280mm?

4 £5.00 – £1.11 =

5 5·45 x 100 =

B 1 One-fifth of a length is 6cm, what is the total length?

2 4·06 x 100 =

3 51 x 3 =

4 Divide £370 by 100.

5 Multiply 26 by 4.

C 1 One-seventh of a number is 16, what is the number?

2 How many seconds in 1 hour?

3 6·030 x 1000 =

4 What is 7% of £50?

5 £3.29 + £4.96 =

TEST 19

A 1 Which is longer an inch or a centimetre?

2 0·6m + 0·9m =

3 3·821 x 10 =

4 How much is one-fifth of £1.00?

5 Divide 67 by 10.

B 1 48 x 2 =

2 0·424 x 100 =

3 –6 – 3 =

4 One-ninth of a number is 6, what is the number?

5 Divide £6700 by 100.

C 1 How much is 12% of a metre?

2 One-fifth of an amount is £2.50, what is the amount?

3 Reduce 8 by 12.

4 Multiply 70·070 by 1000.

5 What is the size of angle x?

A1 42 ÷ 10 =

2 £2.00 + £1.10 + £1.20 =

3 41·24 x 10 =

4 $\frac{1}{5}$ of 25 =

5 How much is £2.50 + £3.50 + £4.50?

B1 How many degrees are the same as three right angles?

2 381·62 x 100 =

3 One-third of some money is 40p, how much is the total amount?

4 26 x 2 =

5 Share £6.30 amongst 10.

C1 What is 21% of £50?

2 Multiply 0·076 by 1000.

3 One-third of a distance is 40cm, what is the total distance?

4 46 x 3 =

5 How many lines of symmetry does an equilateral triangle have?

A1 Reduce £30.00 by £10.50.

2 How much is one-third of 60?

3 What size is the missing angle?

4 Divide 690 by 100.

5 5·76 x 10 =

B1 How far is $\frac{1}{5}$ of a kilometre?

2 Divide 6260 by 100.

3 £4.00 − £0.63 =

4 426·10 x 100 =

5 65 x 2 =

C1 One-fifth of a distance is 24cm what is the total distance?

2 29 x 3 =

3 What is 38% of 2 metres?

4 Multiply 3·006 by 100.

5 If three hot dogs cost £1.50, how much will seven cost?

When we divide by 10, 100 or 1000 we can easily see that the numbers have become smaller because of the position of the decimal point.

Look at these examples:

$125 \cdot 6 \div 10 = 12 \cdot 56$
$125 \cdot 6 \div 100 = 1 \cdot 256$
$125 \cdot 6 \div 1000 = 0 \cdot 1256$

Notice that when we divide by 10, the decimal point moves one place to the left from 125·6 to 12·56.

When we divide by 100, the decimal point moves two places to the left from 125·6 to 1·256.

The decimal point moves the same number of places as there are zeros in the number we divide by.

Look at these examples:

$2671 \cdot 6 \div 10 = 267 \cdot 16$

Because 10 has a single zero the point moves only one place to the left.

$2671 \cdot 6 \div 100 = 26 \cdot 716$

Because 100 has two zeros, the point moves two places to the left.

$2671 \cdot 6 \div 1000 = 2 \cdot 6716$

Because 1000 has three zeros, the point moves three places to the left.

A 1 $21 \cdot 9 \div 10 =$

2 $36 \cdot 8 \div 10 =$

3 $73 \cdot 6 \div 10 =$

4 $129 \cdot 4 \div 100 =$

5 $361 \cdot 7 \div 100 =$

B 1 $0 \cdot 8 \div 10 =$

2 $326 \cdot 5 \div 10 =$

3 $47 \cdot 0 \div 100 =$

4 $325 \cdot 46 \div 100 =$

5 $496 \cdot 12 \div 1000 =$

C 1 $3 \cdot 08 \div 10 =$

2 $0 \cdot 72 \div 10 =$

3 $300 \cdot 6 \div 100 =$

4 $503 \cdot 06 \div 100 =$

5 $267 \cdot 43 \div 1000 =$

TEST 23

A1 What is one-third of 30?

2 $4{\cdot}9 \div 10 =$

3 What is the total of 1·30m and 2·80m?

4 What temperature comes next: 6°, 4°, 2°, 0° ?

5 $6{\cdot}1 \times 10 =$

B1 What is 2·56 divided by 10?

2 A child has £3.00 and spends £1.21, how much does she have left?

3 $13{\cdot}30 \times 100 =$

4 What is 25% of 3 metres?

5 A temperature of 4° goes down by 7°, what is the new temperature?

C1 20% of a number is 8, what is the number?

2 Divide 3671·89 by 1000.

3 $46 \times 3 =$

4 Multiply 42·606 by 1000.

5 Work out the missing angle.

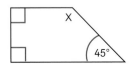

TEST 24

A1 Multiply 4·8 by 10.

2 Reduce 1·46l by 0·34l.

3 Is this angle acute or obtuse?

4 What is one-fifth of 50?

5 Divide 13·2 by 10.

B1 Multiply 21·00 by 100.

2 What is one-ninth of 63p?

3 How many edges does this shape have?

4 $£3.45 \times 2 =$

5 What is 312·8 divided by 100?

C1 Drawing pins cost 0·04p each, how much will 1000 cost?

2 What size are the missing angles?

3 $38 \times 2 =$

4 What is the order of rotation of this shape? △

5 Divide 27686·3 by 1000.

A 1   2·3 ÷ 10 =

2   Subtract 0·62 from 1·00.

3   Multiply 41·9 by 10.

4   What is 10% of 30p?

5   £4.60 − £3.70 =

B 1   How many faces does this shape have?

2   Reduce 46·23 by 3·18.

3   0·4 ÷ 10 =

4   How many remain when 71 is divided by 8?

5   17·34 x 100 =

C 1   What is twice 57?

2   Divide 46,296·0 by 1000.

3   Does this shape have a line of symmetry ?   N

4   0·006 x 100 =

5   About how many cm are the same as one inch?

A 1   Add 3·80m to 4·40m.

2   What is 10% of 60cm?

3   12·6 divided by 10 equals?

4   Does the letter A have a line of symmetry?

5   6·82 x 10 =

B 1   A man owes £260 and pays back £180. How much does he still owe?

2   Multiply £27.00 by 100.

3   36·62 ÷ 100 =

4   In a class of 30 children, one-tenth are away. How many are present?

5   What is the total 5·62 and 4·88?

C 1   Add 3·85m to 67cm

2   Multiply 1000 by 5·005.

3   How many lines of symmetry does this shape have?   ⊥

4   What is the order of rotation of this shape?   Z

5   Divide 3000·0 by 1000.

TEST 27

A 1   0·32 x 10 =

  2   What is one-quarter of 36?

  3   Multiply £4.60 by 2.

  4   12·8 ÷ 10 =

  5   How many lines
    of symmetry does
    this shape have?

B 1   Multiply 200·16 by 100.

  2   How many hours in 3 days?

  3   Divide 37·8 by 100.

  4   Divide £6.00 by 5.

  5   $700 \times \frac{1}{10} =$

C 1   6200·3 ÷ 1000 =

  2   How many are 5 dozen?

  3   60·606 multiplied by 1000 =

  4   75% of a number is 15, what is
    the number?

  5   Multiply 46 by 2.

TEST 28

A 1   Multiply £5.70 by 2.

  2   What temperature comes next?
    −10°, −8°, −6° ?

  3   3·02 ÷ 10 =

  4   What is 10% of 80p?

  5   Multiply 1·06 by 10.

B 1   Out of 48 apples, one-third are
    rotten, how many are good?

  2   What is 431·6 divided by 100?

  3   How many edges does this
    shape have?

  4   4·821 x 100 =

  5   Share £1.35 by 3.

C 1   If 6 eggs cost 72p, how much
    will 1 dozen cost?

  2   Add 67p and £1.40.

  3   Divide 368·24 by 1000.

  4   What sizes
    are angles x
    and y?

  5   Multiply 0·033 by 1000.

A 1 Add 0·70m and 0·80m.

2 3·46 x 10 =

3 What is one-third of 27?

4 Multiply 200·62 by 10.

5 60·1 ÷ 10 =

B 1 How many faces does this shape have?

2 Multiply 3·126 by 1000.

3 One-third of a number is 15, what is the number?

4 Divide 46·0 by 100.

5 Share £10.00 equally amongst 4 children.

C 1 30·678km x 1000 =

2 How much is £120 divided by 15?

3 What is 71,892·36 divided by 1000?

4 How many lines of symmetry does this shape have?

5 How many corners does this shape have?

A 1 What is 50% of £3.00?

2 3·26 ÷ 10 =

3 How many degrees in half a right angle?

4 Multiply 18·7 by 10.

5 How many lines of symmetry does this shape have?

B 1 A drawer contains 60 glass tubes, one-third are cracked. How many are not cracked?

2 Divide 326·7 by 100.

3 Cassettes cost £2.34, how much will 3 cost?

4 36·82 x 100 =

5 Which is farther 1 mile or 1 kilometre?

C 1 Multiply 31·004 by 1000.

2 Lengths of railway track are 18·75m long. How long will 3 lengths be?

3 How many curved faces does this shape have?

4 Divide 126·8km by 1000.

5 How many centimetres is 0·02 metres?

A1   0·672 ÷ 10 =

2   What is the correct name for this shape?

3   8·03 x 10 =

4   Add 1·24cm and 2·36m.

5   What is one-fifth of £40.00?

B1   If a blank video costs £3.67, how much will 2 cost?

2   336·6 ÷ 100 =

3   How many degrees in a quadrilateral?

4   Multiply 32·424 by 100.

5   600 x $\frac{1}{4}$ =

C1   What is 1000 times 6·874?

2   A temperature of −6° goes down by a further 6°, what is the new temperature?

3   3728·632 ÷ 1000 =

4   A stick 3·64m long has 1·87m cut off, how much is left?

5   How many corners does this shape have?

A1   What is 10% of 3 metres?

2   How many edges does this shape have?

3   1·48 ÷ 10 =

4   Which weighs more, a kilogram or a pound?

5   Multiply 0·4 by 10.

B1   4kg of kiwi fruit cost £5.60, how much will 1kg cost?

2   316·266 x 100 =

3   A lady spends three-quarters of £120 on food. How much is that?

4   406·2 ÷ 100 =

5   How many edges does this shape have?

C1   Work units are 1·65m long, how long will 5 units be?

2   What is the total of £2.60, £2.70 and £2.80?

3   42876·1 ÷ 100 =

4   How many corners does a cone have?

5   Multiply 1·489km by 1000.

It is usually easy to find one fractional part of a number.

Example: one-third ($\frac{1}{3}$) of 9 is 3.

It is a bit more complicated to find more than one fractional part. This is how we do it.

Example: to find two-thirds of 15

1 First find one third of 15→5.

2 We do not want one-third, we want two-thirds, so multiply the 5 by 2→10.

3 So two-thirds of 15 is 10.

Example: What is $\frac{4}{5}$ of 25?

1 First find one-fifth of 25→5.

2 We do not want one-fifth, we want four-fifths, so multiply the 5 by 4→20.

3 So four-fifths of 25 is 20.

Example: What is seven-eighths ($\frac{7}{8}$) of 48?

1 First find one-eighth of 48→6.

2 We do not want one-eighth, we want seven-eighths, so multiply the 6 by 7→42.

3 So seven-eighths of 48 is 42.

A 1 What is $\frac{2}{3}$ of 12?

2 How much is $\frac{3}{4}$ of 16?

3 What is $\frac{2}{3}$ of 6?

4 Find $\frac{3}{4}$ of 20.

5 What is $\frac{2}{5}$ of 10?

B 1 What is three-quarters of 24?

2 Find $\frac{4}{5}$ of 30.

3 What is two-thirds of 27?

4 How much is three-fifths of £30?

5 What is three-tenths of 70?

C 1 Find three-eighths of 24.

2 How far is four-fifths of 100km?

3 What is five-ninths of £63.00?

4 Find nine-tenths of £270.00

5 What is three-quarters of 80km?

TEST 34

A1 What is $\frac{2}{3}$ of 18?

  2 3·5 x 10 =

  3 What size is angle x?

  4 32 x 2 =

  5 If 4 milk shakes cost £1.60, how much does each shake cost?

B1 How many edges does this shape have?

  2 Find $\frac{3}{4}$ of £28.00.

  3 5·69 ÷ 10 =

  4 Is an obtuse angle more or less than a right angle?

  5 65p x 3 =

C1 Divide £23.80 by 10.

  2 Three angles of a quadrilateral add up to 270°, what is the size of the 4th angle?

  3 How far is eight-ninths of 81km?

  4 Multiply 162 by 20.

  5 How much is 6000 divided by 20?

TEST 35

A1 47 x 2 =

  2 What size is angle x?

  3 What is $\frac{3}{4}$ of 16?

  4 If 7 doughnuts cost 63p, how much does each doughnut cost?

  5 4·81 x 100 =

B1 48p x 3 =

  2 16·8 ÷ 100 =

  3 What size is angle x?

  4 What is $\frac{3}{4}$ of £4.00?

  5 How many faces does this shape have?

C1 Multiply 135 by 20.

  2 How much is 7000 divided by 35?

  3 What is 154·2m divided by 100?

  4 If 7 apricots cost 84p, how much will 6 apricots cost?

  5 How much is four-fifths of 200 litres?

A1 37·2 ÷ 10 =

2 How many lines of symmetry does this shape have?

3 What is $\frac{2}{3}$ of 30?

4 If 5 apples cost 60p, how much does each apple cost?

5 Multiply 18 by 3.

B1 How many corners does this shape have?

2 What is two-fifths of 35?

3 Multiply 17·05m by 100

4 £6.31 + £4.59 =

5 What is £35 multiplied by 4?

C1 How many 50s are the same as 4000?

2 What is three-quarters of 60?

3 Divide one million by one thousand.

4 If 6kg of bananas cost £3.60, how much will 2kg cost?

5 If a packet contains 160 seeds, how many seeds will there be in 8 packets?

A1 How much are three lots of 25p?

2 How much is $\frac{3}{4}$ of 20?

3 4·89 x 10 =

4 How many hours in 5 whole days?

5 If 9 photocopies cost 36p, how much did each one cost?

B1 How much is 4 times £130?

2 How many faces does this shape have?

3 How much is three-fifths of £30?

4 What is the order of rotation of this shape?

5 Multiply 32·06l by 10

C1 How many 20p pieces are the same as £30.00?

2 What is 2776·0 ÷ 1000?

3 What number multiplied by 8 gives an amount of 240?

4 How much is nine-tenths of £50?

5 How many degrees is angle x?

A 1 What number multiplied by 4 gives the answer 44?

2 Name this shape.

3 What is $\frac{2}{3}$ of 3?

4 If 8 eggs cost 72p, how much will 1 egg cost?

5 4·81 x 10 =

B 1 One-third of a number is 7, what is the number?

2 How many edges does this shape have?

3 Divide 130·0 by 10.

4 What number multiplied by 12, gives the answer 84?

5 Subtract 260 from 1000.

C 1 How many 18s are the same as 360?

2 Two-thirds of a number is 6. What is the number?

3 What is half of 192?

4 How many metres are the same as 4672cm?

5 What amount multiplied by 14 gives the answer £280.00?

A 1 How much is $\frac{3}{4}$ of £32.00?

2 377·0 ÷ 100 =

3 How many degrees in half a right angle?

4 What number multiplied by 5 gives the answer 60?

5 If 50 pencils cost £3.00, how much does each pencil cost?

B 1 What number multiplied by 20 gives the answer 400?

2 Arrange these numbers in order, starting with the lowest, 8, –3, 2, 3, –6.

3 One-fifth of a number if 7. What is the number?

4 How many triangular faces does a square-based pyramid have?

5 What is £260.00 divided by 100?

C 1 How many litres are the same as 63,000ml?

2 What amount multiplied by 30 gives the answer 1200?

3 Multiply 260 by 5.

4 Three-fifths of a number is 12. What is the number?

5 What is a half of 265?

A1 Reduce 100 by 67.

2 How much is $\frac{2}{3}$ of 21?

3 Does the letter **F** have a line of symmetry?

4 2·9 x 10 =

5 What number multiplied by 8 gives the answer 160?

B1 Reduce 62 by half.

2 One-ninth of a number is 8. What is the number?

3 −4 − 3 =

4 Divide 205·3 by 100.

5 What number divided by 9 gives the answer 100?

C1 Two-thirds of a number is 20, what is the number?

2 How many degrees in one and a half right angles?

3 What is half of £370.00?

4 What number divided by 20 gives the answer 20?

5 Share £2764 equally amongst 10 people.

A1 What number multiplied by 6 gives the answer 3?

2 0·37 ÷ 10 =

3 If 6 rubbers cost 48p, how much will 3 rubbers cost?

4 How much is $\frac{3}{4}$ of 40?

5 Add 24, 24 and 24.

B1 One-sixth of a number is 7, what is the number?

2 What is the order of rotation of 6?

3 What is one-tenth of £37.00?

4 How much is 75% of £600?

5 Subtract 7 from 4.

C1 How many 100s are the same as one hundred thousand?

2 What number divided by 15 gives the answer 4?

3 If 4kg of peaches cost £4.36, how much will 3kg cost?

4 Two-sixths of a number is 8, what is the number?

5 Which is longer a metre or a yard?

A1 Total 20, 30 and 40.

2 What is $\frac{3}{4}$ of 20cm?

3 How many lines of symmetry does the letter I have?

4 0·27 x 10 =

5 What number divided by 6 gives the answer 20?

B1 What is 2·5 multiplied by 3?

2 Multiply 27·71 by 100.

3 How many edges does a sphere have?

4 One-seventh of a number is 7. What is the number?

5 What number divided by 9 gives the answer 30?

C1 Multiply 160 by 9.

2 Divide 6·5 by 5.

3 Two-thirds of a number is 24. What is the number?

4 A number multiplied by 35 is 700. What is the number?

5 What is 67,340cm written as metres?

A1 What number divided by 4 gives the answer 40?

2 0·38 x 100 =

3 How much is $\frac{2}{3}$ of £12.00?

4 What is the order of rotation of the number 8?

5 Divide 180 by 3.

B1 Divide £3700 by 1000.

2 Multiply 4·8 by 2.

3 One-fifth of a number is 6, what is the number?

4 −6 + 10 =

5 What number divided by 12 gives the answer 11?

C1 How many kilometres are the same as 48,274 metres?

2 How many halves are the same as $13\frac{1}{2}$?

3 How much is 8 times £32.00?

4 Three-sevenths of a number is 18, what is the number?

5 Multiply 38 by 30.

It is sometimes useful to be able to find the mean (average of a group of numbers or amounts)
EXAMPLE: Find the mean (average) amount of pocket money of 6 children. This is how much the children get each week:

£5, £3, £3, £4, £3, £3.

To find the mean:

1 Add the amounts
£5 + £3 + £3 + £4 + £3 + £3 = £21.

2 Divide the total amount by the number of children £21 ÷ 6 = £3.50.

3 So the average amount is £3.50.

EXAMPLE: Find the mean temperature over 4 days
These are the temperatures: 18° 21° 24° 23°.

To find the mean:

1 Add the temperatures 18° + 21° + 24° + 23° = 86°.

2 Divide the total temperature by the number of days 86° ÷ 4 = 21·5°.

3 So the average temperature was 21·5°.

EXAMPLE: Find the mean of this list of numbers: 2, 7, 0, 3.

1 Add the numbers: 2 + 7 + 0 + 3 = 12.

2 Divide the total by 4: notice that we divide by 4 not 3 because the zero counts as a number.
12 ÷ 4 = 3.

3 So the average of the numbers is 3.

TEST 44

A Find the mean of each list.

1 6p, 9p, 8p, 5p.

2 10cm, 3cm, 5cm.

3 5kg, 7kg, 4kg, 4kg.

4 20°, 18°, 16°.

5 2m, 3m, 4m.

B Find the mean of each list.

1 £12, £5, £10, £9.

2 120cm, 78cm.

3 25, 10, 13.

4 6·5, 4·5, 4.

5 31, 28, 25.

C Find the mean of each list.

1 3, 7, 2, 8, 10.

2 5m, 3m, 2·8m, 4·2m.

3 6°, 0°, 8°, 10°.

4 42, 20, 10.

5 13, 17, 0, 6, 0, 0.

A 1 8·8 x 10 =

2 What is the mean of 3, 4 and 5?

3 2·5 x 2 =

4 How much is $\frac{1}{3}$ of £30?

5 How many lines of symmetry does this shape have?

B 1 3·8 x 2 =

2 Find the mean of 14, 12 and 7.

3 3·88 ÷ 10 =

4 How much is one-seventh of £42?

5 £4·62 x 2 =

C 1 The mean of two numbers is 7. One of the numbers is 9, what is the other number?

2 3700km ÷ 1000 =

3 £4.62 + £3.39 =

4 Multiply 62 by 5.

5 Three-eighths of a number is 15. What is the number?

A 1 4·6 x 2 =

2 What is $\frac{1}{5}$ of £5?

3 How many flat surfaces does a cylinder have?

4 9·25 x 100 =

5 Find the mean of 10cm, 4cm and 7cm.

B 1 How far is two-sixths of 18km?

2 Divide 24·4 by 10.

3 How much is 20% of £500?

4 What is the mean of 2, 1 and 3?

5 What size is angle x?

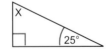

C 1 Four fifths of a number is 16, what is the number?

2 £10.00 − £3.28 =

3 The mean of two numbers is 5, one of the numbers is 2, what is the other number?

4 How many litres are the same as 20,431ml?

5 How many degrees is angle x?

A1 What is the mean of £10, £4 and £1?

2 Does acute mean more or less than a right angle?

3 $27 \cdot 4 \times 10 =$

4 How much is two-thirds of 9?

5 $5 \cdot 5 \times 2 =$

B1 Divide $380 \cdot 0$ by 100.

2 $4 - 6 =$

3 Find the mean of 18, 6 and 9.

4 £2.62 + £2.08 =

5 How far is $\frac{3}{4}$ of 1000km?

C1 Out of 60 oranges only four-fifths are ripe, how many are not ripe?

2 $23 \div 2 =$

3 What is 62 divided by 100?

4 A temperature of $-4°$ rises by $6°$, what is the temperature now?

5 Find the mean of £12, £10, £10 and £16.

A1 $61 \div 2 =$

2 Find the mean of 6, 3 and 9.

3 $6 \cdot 9 + 0 \cdot 7 + 3 \cdot 1 =$

4 Multiply $0 \cdot 77$ by 100.

5 What is three-quarters of 16?

B1 A third of a number is 12, what is the number?

2 A temperature of $3°$ goes down by $4°$, what is the temperature now?

3 £5.00 − £1.61 =

4 What is the mean of 3, 5, 6 and 4?

5 Divide $69 \cdot 0$ by 100.

C1 Divide $0 \cdot 72$ by 1000.

2 The average of two numbers is 11, one of the numbers is 10, what is the other?

3 $47 \div 2 =$

4 Of 100 cars in a survey $\frac{9}{10}$ were made in Japan. How many were not made in Japan?

5 If 8 glasses cost £36, how much will 3 cost?

A 1 What is the mean of 2, 1, 3 and 6?

2 £3.82 + £0.20 =

3 A quarter of a number is 10, what is the number?

4 £1.70 − £0.69 =

5 342·2 ÷ 100 =

B 1 How many 10s in 100m?

2 What is the average of £25 and £75?

3 720·8 ÷ 10 =

4 A quarter of a number is 3·5, what is the number?

5 −4 − 5 =

C 1 In cricket, one batsman scores 64 runs and another scores 26 runs. What is their average score?

2 If 9 batteries cost £5.40, how much will 10 batteries cost?

3 £3.75 x 2 =

4 Out of 1000 biros, nine-tenths are blue, the rest are red, how many of each colour?

5 Does 3 multiplied by 19 make 57?

A 1 600 x 1000 =

2 A half of a number is 6·5, what is the number?

3 £4.30 + £2.70 =

4 Find the average of 10 and 40.

5 Divide 7 by 2.

B 1 A fifth of the children in a class wear glasses. There are 30 children in the class, how many do not wear glasses?

2 How many are 2 dozen?

3 9 − 20 =

4 Find the mean of 27 and 33.

5 Multiply £23.61 by 1000.

C 1 Two-thirds of a number is 12, what is the number?

2 A boy believes that 12 times 12 is 154, is he correct?

3 Divide £20.00 by 8.

4 What is the difference between −8°C and 8°C?

5 Three ladies run 100m in 10 seconds, 13 seconds, and 10 seconds. What is their mean time?

A Try to answer each section in 30 seconds or less.

1 4·9 x 10 =

2 31·8 ÷ 10 =

3 46·3 x 10 =

4 0·45 x 10 =

5 31·88 ÷ 100 =

B 1 15 x 3 =

2 21 x 4 =

3 90 ÷ 15 =

4 5 ÷ 4 =

5 £3·33 + £2·67 =

C 1 3269·0 ÷ 1000 =

2 0·006 x 100 =

3 £33.66 + £24.33 =

4 £20.00 − £2.70 =

5 What is the mean of 20, 40 and 60?

A Try to answer each section in 30 seconds or less.

1 0·8 x 10 =

2 512·0 ÷ 10 =

3 0·04 x 10 =

4 31·6 ÷ 10 =

5 £2.50 + £2.50 + £2.50 =

B 1 18 x 3 =

2 34 x 3 =

3 48 ÷ 16 =

4 9 ÷ 4 =

5 −7 − 8 =

C 1 37·22 ÷ 100 =

2 £3.00 − £0.35 =

3 135 x 2 =

4 51 ÷ 3 =

5 15% of 300 =

TEST 53

A Try to answer each section in 30 seconds or less.

1 $10 - 11 =$

2 $2{\cdot}5 \times 3 =$

3 $9 \div 2 =$

4 $£46 \div 10 =$

5 $£3.80 \times 10 =$

B 1 $3{\cdot}9 \times 3 =$

2 $2{\cdot}6 \times 4 =$

3 $300 \div 15 =$

4 $131 \times 3 =$

5 $462 \div 2 =$

C 1 $7{\cdot}6 \div 2 =$

2 $3800 \div 1000 =$

3 $£4.00 - £2.22 =$

4 $3{\cdot}56 \times 2 =$

5 $2{\cdot}87m \div 2 =$

TEST 54

A Try to answer each section in 30 seconds or less.

1 $6 - 10 =$

2 $4{\cdot}5 \times 4 =$

3 $13 \div 2 =$

4 $£270 \div 100 =$

5 $£5.69 \times 10 =$

B 1 $4{\cdot}6 \times 2 =$

2 $3{\cdot}8 \times 2 =$

3 $480 \div 16 =$

4 $154 \times 3 =$

5 $701 \div 2 =$

C 1 $57 \div 3 =$

2 20% of $60 =$

3 $\frac{2}{3}$ of $90 =$

4 $£1.09 - £0.91 =$

5 $1{\cdot}45m + 0{\cdot}77m =$

A1 How many degrees in two right angles?

2 3·5 x 3 =

3 What number subtracted from 40 leaves 18?

4 54 ÷ 2 =

5 What is the mean of 1, 3 and 11?

B1 What size is the missing angle?

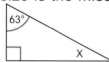

2 6·83 x 3 =

3 How many edges does a cuboid have?

4 Are these two lines parallel?

5 How much is 25% of 5km?

C1 What number multiplied by 1·5 gives 9?

2 How many sides are the same length in an isosceles triangle?

3 The mean of 3 numbers is 8, two of the numbers are 12 and 4, what is the third number?

4 524 x 3 =

5 Put the letter A on this line to show the probability that a thrown dice will land with an even number upwards.

```
L_____|_____|_____|_____|
0        ·25       ·5       ·75       1
```

A1 8⟌60

2 Name this shape.

3 If a number multiplied by 12 is 84, what is the number?

4 4·2 x 5 =

5 How many minutes in 4 hours?

B1 How many hours in 3 days?

2 12 ÷ 5 =

3 What number subtracted from 80 leaves 33?

4 4·29 x 3 =

5 What is the mean of 3, 5, 7 and 9?

C1 How much is 30% of £60.00?

2 213 x 20 =

3 What number multiplied by 100 gives 3760?

4 240 ÷ 12 =

5 What is the size of each angle of an equilateral triangle?

A1   1·7 x 3 =

2   How many degrees in a full turn?

3   3·81 x 10 =

4   What number added to 19 gives 44?

5   569·6 ÷ 100 =

B1   What is three-fifths of 40?

2   6·61 x 2 =

3   What number multiplied by 24 gives 120?

4   34,269 ÷ 1000 =

5   How many lines of symmetry does the number **3** have?

C1   How long is three-fifths of 1 hour?

2   What size is angle x?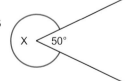

3   364 x 11 =

4   −10 + 6 =

5   The mean of three numbers is 9, two of the numbers are 7 and 4, what is the third number?

A1   How many faces does this shape have?

2   72·60 x 100 =

3   What number subtracted from 82 gives 48?

4   2·8 x 3 =

5   What number multiplied by 8 gives 160?

B1   What is the order of rotation of this shape?

2   What size is angle x?

3   What is two-fifths of £2.00?

4   4·23 x 3 =

5   Which is more a litre or a pint?

C1   260 x 3 =

2   What size is angle x?

3   What number when multiplied by 12 gives 15?

4   −4 − 5 =

5   How far is seven-eighths of 400km?

A1   28 x 100 =

2   How many degrees in half a right angle?

3   Find $\frac{1}{4}$ of 40.

4   80 ÷ 10 =

5   How many mm in 3·5cm?

B1   What is 34 divided by 10?

2   Multiply 6·8 by 1000.

3   Divide £37 by 10.

4   How many grams are the same as 1·723kg?

5   Write these numbers in order with the smallest first:
4, −3, 7, 0, −5.

C1   How much is seven-eighths of 72 hours?

2   Divide 480 by 16.

3   A number multiplied by 7 makes 154. What is the number?

4   Two angles of a triangle add up to 106°. What is the size of the third angle?

5   What is 90% of 60 litres?

A1   What is three quarters of 24?

2   What is the mean of 8 and 12?

3   7·5 x 100 =

4   What size is angle x?

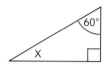

5   140 ÷ 10 =

B1   3·9 x 4 =

2   What is $\frac{2}{5}$ of 35?

3   $4\overline{)23}$

4   How many degrees in three-quarters of a full turn?

5   What is £2.06 times 1000?

C1   How far is 75% of 1km?

2   If 6 apples cost 48p, how much will 5 apples cost?

3   What is two-thirds of £60.00?

4   What number subtracted from 200 leaves 127?

5   Draw the probability scale and label where 'EVEN' is on it.